2 Describe fully each of the numbered and bracketed melodic intervals (e

Intervals:

1 ....

2 ....

3 ....

4 ....

5 ....

3 The following melody is written for horn in F. Transpose it *down* a perfect 5th, as it will  sound at concert pitch. Do *not* use a key signature but remember to put in all necessary sharp, flat or natural signs.

Schoenberg, Five Orchestral Pieces, Op. 16

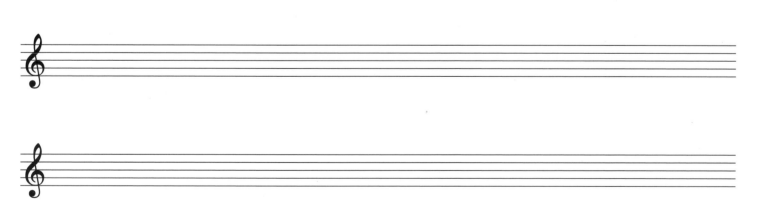

4 Look at this extract from a song by Schubert and then answer the questions that follow.

(a) (i) Give the meaning of **Mässig**. .... (2)

(ii) Give the technical names (e.g. tonic, dominant) of the two notes in the soprano part marked **A** and **B**. The key is A♭ major.

A (bar 1) .... (2)

B (bar 3) .... (2)

(iii) Rewrite the last right-hand piano chord of the extract so that it sounds at the same pitch, but using the tenor C clef. Remember to put in the clef and the key signature.

(4)

(b) (i) Describe the chords marked ⌐X⌐, ⌐Y⌐ and ⌐Z⌐ as I, II, IV or V. Also indicate whether the lowest note of the chord is the root (a), 3rd (b) or 5th (c). Remember the key is A♭ major.

Chord **X** (bar 3) .... (2)

Chord **Y** (bar 3) .... (2)

Chord **Z** (bar 4) .... (2)

[10]

(ii) The extract begins in the key of A♭ major. In what key does it end? .... (2)

(iii) Describe the time signature as: simple or compound .... (1)

duple, triple or quadruple .... (1)

[10]

(c) (i) Which other key has the same key signature as A♭ major? .... (2)

(ii) This extract is from a song written for soprano, which is the highest sounding voice. Rewrite the following voices in order of their pitch range from **highest** to **lowest**. The first answer is given.

Alto   Baritone   Soprano   Bass   Tenor

Soprano
.... (4)

(iii) Name two standard orchestral instruments, one transposing and one non-transposing, which could play the soprano part of the extract so that it sounds at the same pitch.

Transposing .... Non-transposing .... (4)

5 (a) Using semibreves (whole notes), write one octave **descending** of the **melodic** minor scale that begins on the given note. Do *not* use a key signature but put in all necessary sharp or flat signs.

(b) Write the key signature of five flats and then one octave **ascending** of the major scale with that key signature. Use semibreves (whole notes) and begin on the tonic.

6 EITHER

(a) Compose a complete melody for unaccompanied oboe or violin, using the given opening. **Indicate the tempo and other performance directions**, including any that might be particularly required for the instrument chosen. The complete melody should be eight bars long.

Instrument for which the melody is written: ....

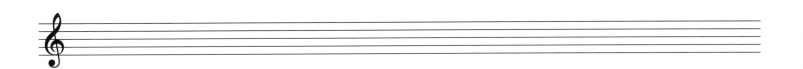

OR

(b) Compose a complete melody to the following words for a solo voice. Write each syllable under the note or notes to which it is to be sung. Also **indicate the tempo and other performance directions as appropriate**.

> We were a gallant company,
> Riding o'er land, and sailing o'er sea.   *Lord Byron*

7 Suggest suitable progressions for two cadences in the following melody by indicating ONLY ONE chord (I, II, IV or V) at each of the places marked A–E. You do not have to indicate the position of the chords, or to state which note is in the bass.

Show the chords:

EITHER (a) by writing I, II etc. or any other recognized symbols on the dotted lines below;

OR   (b) by writing notes on the staves.

FIRST CADENCE:

SECOND CADENCE:

Chord A ....

Chord D ....

Chord B ....

Chord E ....

Chord C ....

BLANK PAGE

Theory Paper Grade 5   2011   B

Duration 2 hours

This paper contains SEVEN questions, ALL of which should be answered.
Write your answers on this paper – no others will be accepted.
Answers must be written clearly and neatly – otherwise marks may be lost.

TOTAL MARKS
100

15

1 (a) Look at the following extract and then answer the questions below.

Adagio sostenuto

Beethoven, Variations on 'Venni amore'

(i) The extract begins on the first beat of the bar. Put in the missing bar-lines.   (3)

(ii) Rewrite the two notes near the end of the extract (marked ⌐___⌐) so that they sound at the same pitch, but using the alto C clef. Remember to put in the clef and the key signature.

(4)

(b) Look at the following extract and then answer the questions below.

Haydn, Piano Trio in A, Hob. XV/18

Andante

mezza voce

etc.

(i) Give the meaning of
mezza (the same as *mezzo*) *voce*. ....   (2)

(ii) Name the two ornaments marked ⌐A⌐ and ⌐B⌐.

A ....   B ....   (4)

(iii) In what key does the extract begin? ....   (2)

2 Describe fully each of the numbered and bracketed melodic intervals (e.g. major 2nd). 10

J. S. Bach, *Bisher habt ihr nichts gebeten*, BWV 87

Intervals:

1 ....

2 ....

3 ....

4 ....

5 ....

3 The following melody is written for clarinet in A. Transpose it *down* a minor 3rd, as it will sound at concert pitch. Do *not* use a key signature but remember to put in all necessary sharp, flat or natural signs.

Wagner, *Tristan und Isolde*

4 Look at this extract from a piano sonata by Mozart and then answer the questions that follow.

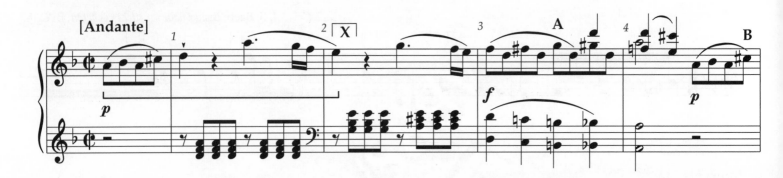

(a) (i) Underline *one* word from the list below that has a similar meaning to **Andante**. 10

  lebhaft   *langsam*   *mässig*   *schnell*   (2)

(ii) Draw a bracket (⌐___⌐) under *four successive* notes that form part of a chromatic scale.   (2)

(iii) The extract begins in the key of D minor. In what key does it end? ....   (2)

(iv) Give the technical names (e.g. tonic, dominant) of the two notes in the right-hand part marked **A** and **B**. Remember that the key is D minor.

  A (bar 3) ....   (2)

  B (bar 4) ....   (2)

(b) (i) Describe the chords marked ⌐X⌐ and ⌐Y⌐ as I, II, IV or V. Also indicate whether the lowest note of the chord is the root (a), 3rd (b) or 5th (c). The key is D minor. [10]

Chord **X** (bar 2) .... (2)

Chord **Y** (bar 5) .... (2)

(ii) Below the staves write Ic–V ($^6_4$ $^5_3$) under the *two successive* chords in bars 1–4 where this progression occurs. (2)

(iii) Rewrite the last left-hand chord of the extract so that it sounds at the same pitch, but using the tenor C clef. Remember to put in the clef and the key signature.

(4)

(c) (i) Rewrite the right-hand opening phrase of the extract (marked ⌐_____⌐) [10] using notes and a rest of *half the value*. Remember to put in the new time signature.

(4)

(ii) Name a standard orchestral woodwind instrument that could play the opening phrase of the extract (marked ⌐_____⌐) so that it sounds at the same pitch.

Instrument .... (2)

(iii) Now name a *different* family of standard orchestral instruments and state its lowest sounding member.

Family .... Instrument .... (4)

5 (a) Using semibreves (whole notes), write one octave **ascending** of the **chromatic** scale [10] that begins on the given note. Remember to put in all necessary sharp, flat or natural signs.

(b) Write the key signature of four flats and then one octave **descending** of the **harmonic** minor scale with that key signature. Use semibreves (whole notes), begin on the tonic and remember to put in any necessary additional sharp, flat or natural signs.

(a) Compose a complete melody for unaccompanied flute or trumpet, using the given opening. **Indicate the tempo and other performance directions**, including any that might be particularly required for the instrument chosen. The complete melody should be eight bars long.

   Instrument for which the melody is written: ....

OR

(b) Compose a complete melody to the following words for a solo voice. Write each syllable under the note or notes to which it is to be sung. Also **indicate the tempo and other performance directions as appropriate**.

   And the hawthorn hedge puts forth its buds,
   And my heart puts forth its pain.   *Rupert Brooke*

7 Suggest suitable progressions for two cadences in the following melody by indicating 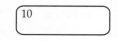ONLY ONE chord (I, II, IV or V) at each of the places marked A–E. You do not have to indicate the position of the chords, or to state which note is in the bass.

Show the chords:

EITHER   (a) by writing I, II etc. or any other recognized symbols on the dotted lines below;

OR   (b) by writing notes on the staves.

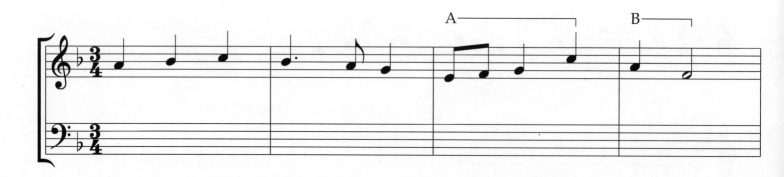

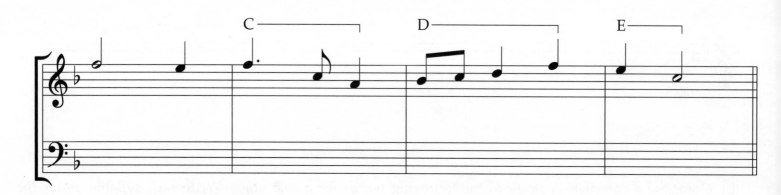

FIRST CADENCE:

Chord A ....

Chord B ....

SECOND CADENCE:

Chord C ....

Chord D ....

Chord E ....

BLANK PAGE

Theory Paper Grade 5   2011   C

Duration 2 hours

This paper contains SEVEN questions, ALL of which should be answered.
Write your answers on this paper – no others will be accepted.
Answers must be written clearly and neatly – otherwise marks may be lost.

TOTAL MARKS
100

15

1 (a) Look at the following extract and then answer the questions below.

Haydn, Piano Sonata in E♭ major, Hob. XVI/38

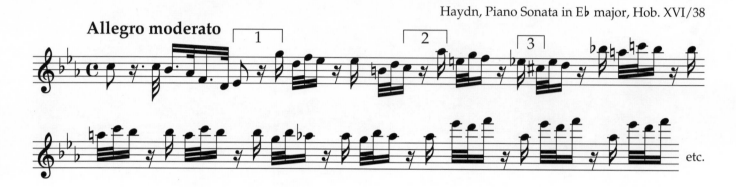

Allegro moderato

(i)   The extract begins on the first beat of the bar. Put in the missing bar-lines.   (3)

(ii)   Describe fully each of the numbered and bracketed melodic intervals (e.g. major 2nd).

    1 ....   (2)

    2 ....   (2)

    3 ....   (2)

(b) Look at the following extract, which begins on the first beat of the bar, and then answer
the questions below.

Howells, *Missa Sabrinensis*

(i)   Put in the correct time signatures at the two places marked ✳.   (4)

(ii)   Write as a breve (double whole-note) an enharmonic equivalent of the first note of bar 2.

(2)

2 This passage is for SATB choir, written in open score. Rewrite it in short score.

Richard Lloyd, *God of Almighty Love*

etc.

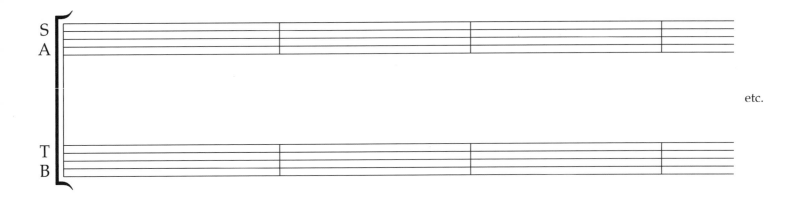

etc.

3 Look at this extract, which is adapted from a sonata for violin and piano by Beethoven, and then answer the questions that follow.

etc.

20

(a) (i) Give the meaning of: [10]

molto moderato e grazioso ....

.... (4)

⊓ (bar 5) .... (2)

sf (bar 7) .... (2)

(ii) Name the ornament in the right-hand piano part of bar 7. .... (2)

(b) (i) Describe the chords marked ⌐X⌐, ⌐Y⌐ and ⌐Z⌐ as I, II, IV or V. Also indicate [10]
whether the lowest note of the chord is the root (a), 3rd (b) or 5th (c).
Regard the key as E♭ major.

Chord **X** (bar 2) .... (2)

Chord **Y** (bar 5) .... (2)

Chord **Z** (bar 6) .... (2)

(ii) Rewrite the first two notes of the violin part so that they sound at the same pitch, but
using the tenor C clef. Remember to put in the clef and the key signature.

(4)

(c) Complete the following statements: [10]

(i) The opening piano right-hand melody
(marked ⌐‾‾‾⌐) is played later by the .... beginning in bar .... (4)

(ii) The violin is the highest sounding member of the .... family of standard

orchestral instruments. Another family of standard orchestral instruments is the

.... and its lowest sounding member is the .... (6)

4 (a) Using semibreves (whole notes), write one octave **ascending** of the **melodic** minor scale that has the given key signature. Begin on the tonic and remember to include any necessary additional sharp, flat or natural signs. [10]

(b) Write one octave **descending** of the scale of A♭ major. Do *not* use a key signature but put in all necessary sharp or flat signs. Use semibreves (whole notes) and begin on the tonic.

5 The following melody is written for clarinet in B♭. Transpose it *down* a major 2nd, as it will sound at concert pitch. Remember to put in the new key signature and add any necessary sharp, flat or natural signs. [10]

Delius, *Appalachia*

(a) Compose a complete melody for unaccompanied cello or bassoon, using the given opening. **Indicate the tempo and other performance directions**, including any that might be particularly required for the instrument chosen. The complete melody should be eight bars long.

Instrument for which the melody is written: ....

OR

(b) Compose a complete melody to the following words for a solo voice. Write each syllable under the note or notes to which it is to be sung. Also **indicate the tempo and other performance directions as appropriate**.

> While the chaffinch sings on the orchard bough
> In England – now!
>
> *Robert Browning*

7 Suggest suitable progressions for two cadences in the following melody by indicating
   ONLY ONE chord (I, II, IV or V) at each of the places marked A–E. You do not have to
   indicate the position of the chords, or to state which note is in the bass.

Show the chords:

EITHER   (a) by writing I, II etc. or any other recognized symbols on the dotted lines below;

OR   (b) by writing notes on the staves.

FIRST CADENCE:

Chord A ....

Chord B ....

SECOND CADENCE:

Chord C ....

Chord D ....

Chord E ....

Theory Paper Grade 5   2011   S

Duration 2 hours

This paper contains SEVEN questions, ALL of which should be answered.
Write your answers on this paper – no others will be accepted.
Answers must be written clearly and neatly – otherwise marks may be lost.

TOTAL MARKS
100

1 (a) The following extract, which begins on the first beat of the bar, contains some
changes of time signature. Put in the correct time signature at each of the three
places marked *.

15

Howells, *Stabat Mater*

etc.

(6)

(b) Look at the following extract and then answer the questions below.

Ravel, *Daphnis et Chloé*, Suite No. 2

Très lent

retenu légèrement

etc.

(i) Give the meaning of:

retenu .... (2)

légèrement .... (2)

(ii) The extract begins on the first beat of the bar. Put in the missing bar-lines. (3)

(iii) Write as a breve (double whole-note) an enharmonic equivalent of the last note of the
extract.

(2)

2 Describe fully each of the numbered and bracketed melodic intervals (e.g. major 2nd). [10]

J. S. Bach, Violin Sonata in E minor, BWV 1023

etc.

Intervals:

1 ....

2 ....

3 ....

4 ....

5 ....

3 The following melody is written for horn in F. Transpose it *down* a perfect 5th, as it will [10]
sound at concert pitch. Do *not* use a key signature but remember to put in all necessary
sharp, flat or natural signs.

Mahler, Symphony No. 9

etc.

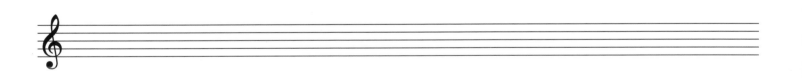

4 Look at this extract adapted from a piano sonata by Haydn and then answer the questions that follow.

(a) (i) **Mark clearly on the music**, using the appropriate capital letter for identification, one example of each of the following. Also give the bar number of each of your answers, as shown in the answer to **A**.

      A   a tie. Bar ....6....

      B   a turn. Bar ....   (2)

      C   a bar that has the same notes and rhythm as
          another bar in this extract but an octave lower. Bar ....   (2)

  (ii) The key of the extract is C minor.
       Which other key has the same key signature? ....   (2)

  (iii) Give the technical names (e.g. tonic, dominant) of the two notes in the right-hand part of bar 3 marked **1** and **2**. Remember the key is C minor.

      1 ....   **2** ....   (4)

(b) (i) Describe the chords marked ⌐X⌐ and ⌐Y⌐ as I, II, IV or V. Also indicate whether [10] the lowest note of the chord is the root (a), 3rd (b) or 5th (c). The key is C minor.

Chord **X** (bar 5) .... (2)

Chord **Y** (bar 6) .... (2)

(ii) Below the staves write Ic–V ($^6_4$ $^5_3$) under *two successive* chords where this progression occurs. (2)

(iii) Rewrite the first right-hand chord of bar 5 so that it sounds at the same pitch, but using the tenor C clef. Remember to put in the clef and the key signature.

(4)

(c) (i) Name a standard orchestral instrument that could play the right-hand part from [10] bar 6 to the end of the extract so that it sounds at the same pitch, and state the family of orchestral instruments to which it belongs.

Instrument .... Family .... (4)

(ii) Now state whether the instrument you named above is a transposing or non-transposing instrument. .... (2)

(iii) Now name a *different* family of standard orchestral instruments and state its lowest sounding member.

Family .... Instrument .... (4)

5 (a) Put sharps or flats in front of the notes that need them to form the scale of Eb **harmonic** minor. Do *not* use a key signature.

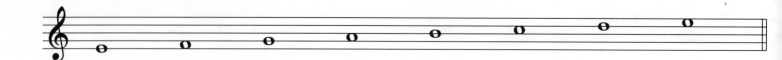

(b) Write the key signature of five sharps and then one octave **descending** of the major scale with that key signature. Use semibreves (whole notes) and begin on the tonic.

6 EITHER

(a) Compose a complete melody for unaccompanied oboe or trumpet, using the given opening. **Indicate the tempo and other performance directions**, including any that might be particularly required for the instrument chosen. The complete melody should be eight bars long.

Instrument for which the melody is written: ....

OR

(b) Compose a complete melody to the following words for a solo voice. Write each syllable under the note or notes to which it is to be sung. Also **indicate the tempo and other performance directions as appropriate**.

The sun was shining on the sea,
Shining with all his might.   *Lewis Carroll*

7 Suggest suitable progressions for two cadences in the following melody by indicating ONLY ONE chord (I, II, IV or V) at each of the places marked A–E. You do not have to indicate the position of the chords, or to state which note is in the bass.

Show the chords:

EITHER   (a)   by writing I, II etc. or any other recognized symbols on the dotted lines below;

OR   (b)   by writing notes on the staves.

FIRST CADENCE:

Chord A ....

Chord B ....

Chord C ....

SECOND CADENCE:

Chord D ....

Chord E ....

ABRSM
24 Portland Place
London W1B 1LU
United Kingdom

www.abrsm.org

Published by ABRSM (Publishing) Ltd,
a wholly owned subsidiary of ABRSM

Printed in England by Halstan & Co. Ltd,
Amersham, Bucks

ISBN 978-1-84849-371-

9 781848 493711